Getty-Dubay
ITALIC HANDWRITING SERIES

Book F

Basic & Cursive Italic

Fourth Edition

by
Barbara Getty & Inga Dubay

Getty-Dubay Productions
Portland, Oregon USA

GETTY-DUBAY ITALIC HANDWRITING SERIES

BOOK A ▪ Basic Italic
14 mm body height

BOOK B ▪ Basic Italic
11 mm, 9 mm body height

BOOK C ▪ Basic & Cursive Italic
9 mm, 6 mm body height   Introduction to Cursive Italic

BOOK D ▪ Basic & Cursive Italic
6 mm, 5 mm body height

BOOK E ▪ Basic & Cursive Italic
6 mm, 5 mm, 4 mm body height

BOOK F ▪ Basic & Cursive Italic
6 mm, 5 mm, 4 mm body height

BOOK G ▪ Basic & Cursive Italic
5 mm, 4 mm body height

INSTRUCTION MANUAL

FOURTH EDITION
Copyright 2012 by Barbara M. Getty and Inga S. Dubay
ISBN 978-0-9649215-5-9

THIRD EDITION
Copyright 1994 by Barbara M. Getty and Inga S. Dubay
SECOND EDITION
Copyright 1986 by Barbara M. Getty and Inga S. Dubay
REVISED EDITION
Copyright 1980 by Barbara M. Getty and Inga S. Dubay
FIRST EDITION
Copyright 1979 by Barbara M. Getty and Inga S. Dubay

15 14 13 12 11
10 9 8 7 6 5 4 3 2 1

Published by Getty-Dubay Productions
Portland, Oregon USA

Distributed by Allport Editions
716 NE Lawrence Avenue
Portland, Oregon 97232 USA
www.allport.com

Printed with vegetable-based, no-VOC inks
on papers containing sustainable-harvest wood fibers and a minimum 30% post-consumer waste.
Printed in the United States of America.

Cover Design: Sinda Markham
Front cover picture: Colorado National Monument Park
Back cover pictures: Ground Squirrels, Prickly Pear Catcus

CONTENTS

INTRODUCTION TO GETTY-DUBAY HANDWRITING

This is the sixth of seven workbooks in the *Getty-Dubay Italic Handwriting Series* and is recommended for fifth grade. This book is designed to provide further practice with cursive capitals and lowercase joins. For the student new to italic handwriting, we provide an introduction to basic italic lowercase and capitals and an overview of the cursive joins.

Writing practice includes vowel sounds, consonant sounds, prefixes, suffixes, and other letter combinations. Sentence content includes word origins, word groups and word entertainment (see note below). Cursive capital practice includes origins of our alphabet and names of Native American tribes, nations and communities. Spiral writing, pop-up card design, and envelope making are also presented.

TEACHER/STUDENT INSTRUCTIONS: Writing process, stroke information, directions, notes, reminders, options, and assessments are included in the margins. Further letter and join descriptions and assessment questions are found in the INSTRUCTION MANUAL.

ASSESSMENT: Assessment is the key to improvement. The self-assessment method used enables the student to monitor his or her own progress. STEP 1: the student is asked to LOOK at the writing and affirm what is the best. Questions are asked requiring a yes/no answer. "Yes" is affirmation of a task accomplished. "No" indicates work to be done. STEP 2: the student is asked to PLAN what needs to be improved and how to accomplish this. STEP 3: the student is asked to put the plan into PRACTICE. This *LOOK, PLAN, PRACTICE* format provides self-assessment skills applicable to all learning situations.

The first focus is on letter shape, followed by size, spacing, and slope. Later, the student uses a checklist for shape, size, spacing, and slope. Use the *Slope Guidelines* to enable the student to find a personal slope. Speed is encouraged only after letterforms and joins are learned. *Timed Writing* enables a gradual increase in the number of words written per minute while maintaining comfort and legibility. Repeat *Timed Writing* once a month. *Reading Looped Cursive* provides experience reading another writing style, and comparing its legibility with that of italic handwriting.

CLASSROOM MANAGEMENT: Using direct instruction, present two pages a week with follow-up practice on lined paper. Demonstrate the stroke sequence for letters and joins. This instruction, together with opportunities for integrating handwriting into other areas of curriculum, can provide 20 to 30 minutes of practice three to four times a week. From day one, have DESKSTRIPS and WALL CHART in place. For extra practice, use BLACKLINE MASTERS. Have lined paper available that matches the 5mm and 4mm lines used in this book (see *Reminders*). Ruled line pages at the back of this book and in the INSTRUCTION MANUAL may be duplicated. Provide the opportunity for each student to select a page of his/her best handwriting to include in the student's portfolio.

As the teacher, your interest and enthusiasm are instrumental in helping students attain the goal of legible and neat handwriting. Pleasure in good handwriting is caught, not taught. The enjoyment of good handwriting is shared by both the writer and the reader. Handwriting is a lifelong skill. Good handwriting is a lifelong joy!

N.B. The information source for origins of the alphabet is *Ancient Writing and Its Influence*. A source for writing practice examples is *The New Reading Teacher's Book of Lists;* for further examples from this book see as follows: (Book F pages are in parentheses)

clipped words (p. 17)	page 79
onomatopoeia (p. 18)	page 90
compound words (p. 19)	page 81
contractions (p. l9)	page 82
portmanteau words (p. 20)	page 80
words from names (p. 21)	page 86

words from other languages (p. 21)	pages 88-89
Greek and Latin roots (p. 22)	pages 94-103
homophones (p. 23)	pages 3-11
homographs (p. 24)	pages 12-20
synonyms (p. 25)	page 62
antonyms (p. 25)	page 63
analogies (p. 25)	pages 67-68
word idioms (p. 26)	pages 72-73
similes (p. 27)	page 69
metaphor (p. 27)	page 70
idiomatic expressions (p. 28)	page 71
proverbs (p. 29)	pages 74-75

BASIC & CURSIVE ITALIC ALPHABET

BASIC ITALIC

*All letters written in one stroke unless otherwise indicated. All letters start at the top except lowercase **d** and **e**.*

Aa Bb Cc Dd Ee Ff Gg

Hh Ii Jj Kk Ll Mm

Nn Oo Pp Qq Rr Ss Tt

Uu Vv Ww Xx Yy Zz

0 1 2 3 4 5 6 7 8 9

CURSIVE ITALIC

*All letters written in one stroke unless otherwise indicated. All letters start at the top except lowercase **d** and **e**.*

Aa Bb Cc Dd Ee Ff Gg

ana bnb cnc dnd ene fnf gng
or ene

Hh Ii Jj Kk Ll Mm

hnh ini jnj knk lnl mnm
or knk   *or mnm*

Nn Oo Pp Qq Rr Ss Tt

nnn ono pnp qnq rnr sns tnt
or nnn   *or rnr*   *or sns*

Uu Vv Ww Xx Yy Zz

unu vnv wnw xnx yny znz
or xnx

GETTY-DUBAY ITALIC HANDWRITING REMINDERS

PENCIL HOLD
Use a soft lead pencil (#1 or #2) with an eraser. Hold the pencil with the thumb and index finger, resting on the middle finger. The upper part of the pencil rests near the large knuckle.

REGULAR HOLD

Hold the pencil firmly and lightly. AVOID pinching. To relax your hand, tap the index finger on the pencil three times.

Problem grips such as the 'thumb wrap' (thumb doesn't touch pencil) and the 'death grip' (very tight pencil hold) make it difficult to use the hand's small muscles. To relieve these problems, try this alternative pencil hold.

ALTERNATIVE HOLD

Place the pencil between the index finger and the middle finger. The pencil rests between the index and middle fingers by the large knuckles. Hold the pencil in the regular way at the tips of the fingers.

PAPER POSITION

LEFT-HANDED
If you are left-handed and write with the wrist below the line of writing, turn the paper clockwise so it is slanted to the right as illustrated. If you are left-handed and write with a "hook" with the wrist above the line of writing, turn the paper counter-clockwise so it is slanted to the left as illustrated. (Similar to the right-handed position)

RIGHT-HANDED
If you are right-handed turn the paper counter-clockwise so it is slanted to the left as illustrated.

POSTURE
Rest your feet flat on the floor and keep your back comfortably straight without slumping. Rest your forearms on the desk. Hold the workbook or paper with your non-writing hand so that the writing area is centered in front of you.

LINED PAPER CHOICES
The following choices for lined paper may be used when instructions say use lined paper for practice.

1. Lines 5mm body height on page 55 may be duplicated. These lines can also be used as guidelines under a sheet of unlined paper. Fasten with paper clips.

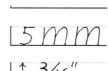

2. Lines 4 mm body height on page 56 may be duplicated. These lines can also be used as a line guide under a sheet of unlined paper. See INSTRUCTION MANUAL pp. 103-104 for lines with capital height.

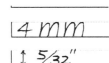

3. Some school paper has a solid baseline and a dotted waistline. Use paper with a body height of 6mm ($^1/_4$") or 5mm ($^3/_{16}$").

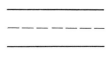

4. Some school paper has only baselines. Use paper with lines 12mm ($^1/_2$") or 10mm ($^3/_8$") apart.

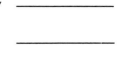

5. Use wide-ruled notebook paper with a space of about 9 mm ($^3/_8$") between lines, or college ruled notebook paper 7.5mm ($^5/_{16}$") between lines. Create your own waistline by lining up two sheets of notebook paper and shifting one down half a space. The faint line showing through will serve as a waistline.

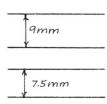

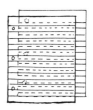

VOCABULARY

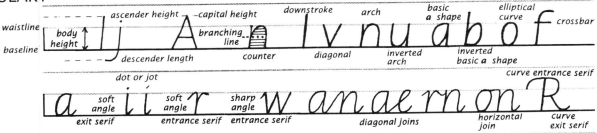

STROKES

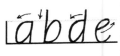

Basic italic letters all start at the top and go down or over (horizontal), except **d** and **e** (**d** starts at the waistline and **e** starts at the center of the body height). Follow the direction of the arrow. Letters are written in one stroke unless otherwise indicated. Trace the dotted line model, then copy model in space provided. If needed, trace solid line model.

LETTER DIMENSIONS

SHAPE

Basic italic lowercase letters are divided into eight families according to shape. Basic italic capitals are divided into three width groups. Cursive italic lowercase joins are divided into eight join groups.

SIZE

Letters are written with a consistent body height. Capitals, ascenders and descenders are written one and a half times the body height.

SLOPE

The models are written with a 5° letter slope. A consistent slope is an important part of good handwriting. For individual slope choices see *Slope Guidelines*, page 44.

SPACING

Letters are written close together within words. Joins are natural spacers in cursive italic; when lifts occur, keep letters close together. Spacing between words is the width of an **n** in basic and cursive italic.

SPEED

Write at a comfortable rate of speed. Though speed is not a primary concern at this level, students may use the *Timed Writing*, page 44.

GOAL
To write legible, neat handwriting.

IMPROVEMENT
Assessment is the key to improving your handwriting. Follow this improvement method as you learn basic and cursive italic handwriting.

 LOOK at your writing. Circle your best letter or join. Answer question about strokes, shape, size, spacing, or slope.

 PLAN how to make your writing look more like the model. Pick the letter or join that needs work. Compare with the model.

 PRACTICE the letter or join that needs work. Write on the lines provided and on lined paper.

 Give yourself a star at the top of the page when you see you have made an improvement.

NOTE: See INSTRUCTION MANUAL, Assessment, pp. 54-68.

INFORMAL ASSESSMENT OF STUDENT PROGRESS

The main purpose of handwriting instruction is to promote legibility so that we can communicate with others and ourselves.

PRE-TEST Before you begin this book, write the following sentence in your everyday handwriting. Also write your name, address and today's date.

A quick brown fox jumps over the lazy dog.

Write the sentence.

1

2

Name

3

Address

4

City, State

5

Today's date

6

POST-TEST After you have completed this workbook, write the following sentence in cursive italic. Also write your name, address and today's date in cursive italic.

A quick brown fox jumps over the lazy dog.

Write the sentence.

7

8

Name

9

Address

10

City, State

11

Today's date

12

ASSESSMENT

SHAPE: Each letter is similar to the models in the workbook.
SIZE: Similar letters are the same height (for example: aec, dhk, gpy). Capital letters and lowercase letters with ascenders are the same height.
SLOPE: Letters have a consistent letter slope (between 5° – 15°).
SPACING: Letters within words are closely spaced. Spaces between words are the width of **n**.
SPEED: Words are written fluently at a comfortable speed.

GETTY-DUBAY BASIC ITALIC

LOWERCASE: 8 families

Family 1. straight line downstroke - i j l
Family 2. diagonal line - k v w x z
Family 3. arch - n h m r
Family 4. inverted arch - u y
Family 5. basic *a* shape - a d g q
Family 6. inverted basic *a* shape - b p
Family 7. elliptical curve - o e c s
Family 8. crossbar - f t

Improvement: shape, size

CAPITALS: 3 width groups

1. wide width - C G O Q D M W
2. medium width - T H A N K U V X Y Z
3. narrow width - E F L B P R S J I

Improvement: shape, size

LOWERCASE AND CAPITALS

Improvement: size, slope, spacing

NUMERALS

abcdefghijklmnopqrstuvwxyz

GETTY-DUBAY BASIC ITALIC LOWERCASE

NOTE:
Can you tell how letters in each family are alike?

NOTE:
All letters start at the top and go down or over, except d and e.

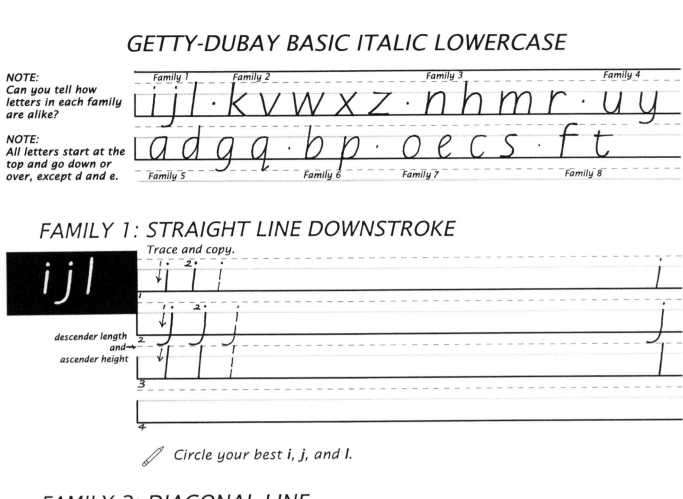

FAMILY 1: STRAIGHT LINE DOWNSTROKE

Trace and copy.

i j l

descender length and → ascender height

✎ Circle your best **i**, **j**, and **l**.

FAMILY 2: DIAGONAL LINE

k v w x z

HINT:
The corner of a sheet of paper fits here. This is a right angle.

baseline

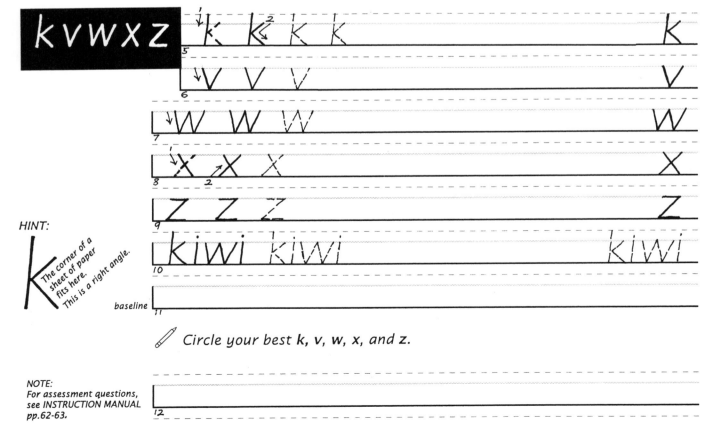

✎ Circle your best **k**, **v**, **w**, **x**, and **z**.

NOTE:
For assessment questions, see INSTRUCTION MANUAL pp.62-63.

FAMILY 3: ARCH

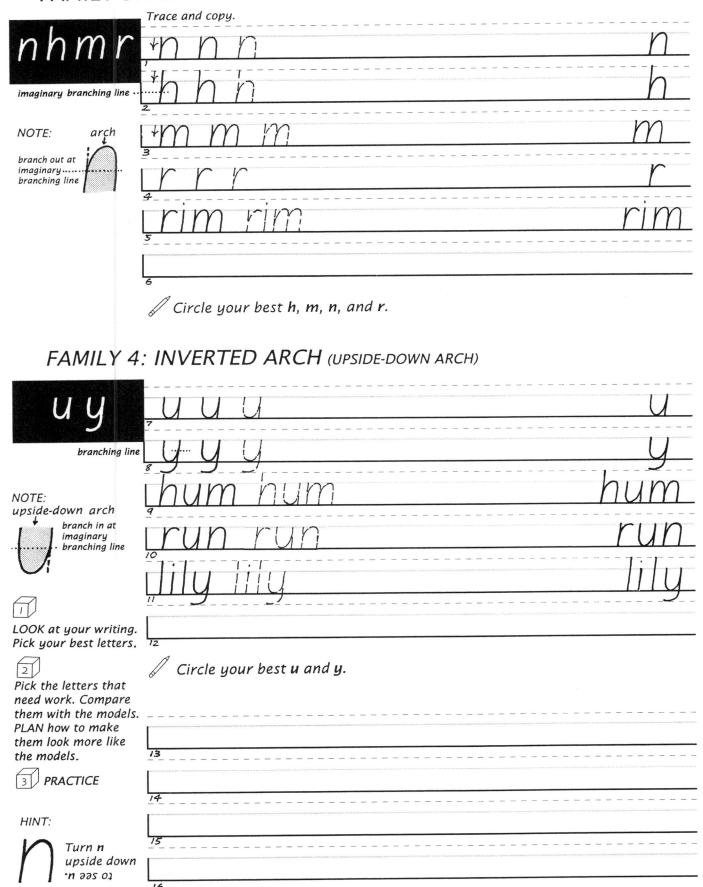

Trace and copy.

nhmr

imaginary branching line

NOTE: arch

branch out at
imaginary
branching line

↓n n n   n

↓h h h   h

↓m m m   m

r r r   r

rim rim   rim

Circle your best **h**, **m**, **n**, and **r**.

FAMILY 4: INVERTED ARCH (UPSIDE-DOWN ARCH)

uy

branching line

NOTE:
upside-down arch

branch in at
imaginary
branching line

u u u   u

y y y   y

hum hum   hum

run run   run

lily lily   lily

1 LOOK at your writing.
Pick your best letters.

2 Pick the letters that
need work. Compare
them with the models.
PLAN how to make
them look more like
the models.

3 PRACTICE

HINT:

n Turn n
upside down
to see u.

Circle your best **u** and **y**.

FAMILY 5: BASIC *a* SHAPE

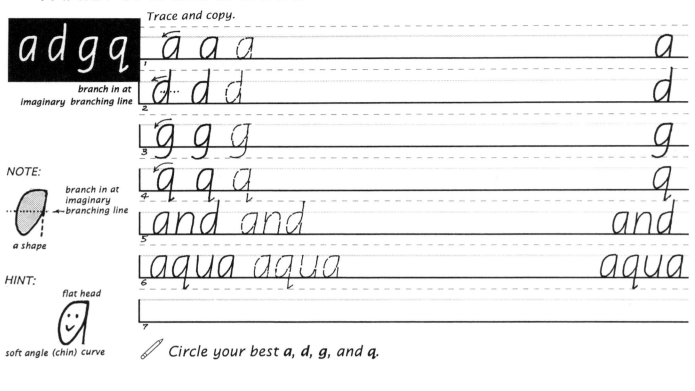

Trace and copy.

branch in at imaginary branching line

NOTE:

branch in at imaginary ←branching line

a shape

HINT:

flat head

soft angle (chin) curve

✏ Circle your best **a**, **d**, **g**, and **q**.

FAMILY 6: INVERTED BASIC *a* SHAPE (UPSIDE-DOWN BASIC *a* SHAPE)

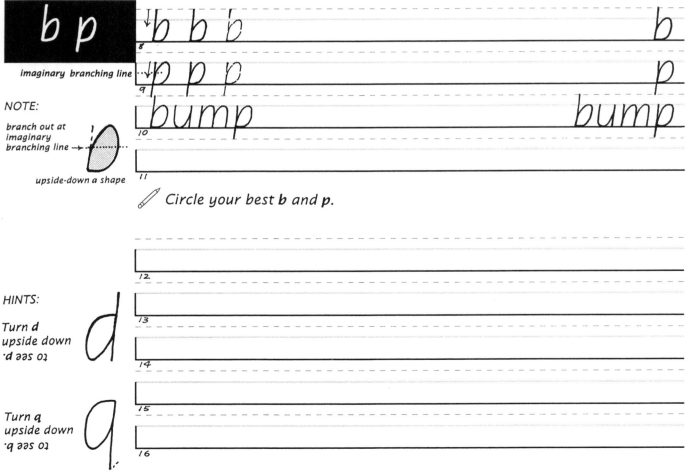

imaginary branching line

NOTE:

branch out at imaginary branching line →

upside-down a shape

✏ Circle your best **b** and **p**.

HINTS:

Turn d upside down to see p.

Turn q upside down to see b.

FAMILY 7: ELLIPTICAL CURVE

Trace and copy.

o e c s

imaginary branching line

o o o   o

e e e   e

c c c   c

s s s   s

oceans oceans   oceans

NOTE:

center of body height

Notice this reads the same right side up as it does upside down.

pod

✏ Circle your best **o**, **e**, **c**, and **s**.

FAMILY 8: CROSSBAR

ft

f f f   f

t t t   t

fast fast   fast

ft ft ft ft   ft

lift lift   lift

NOTE:
The crossbar joins f and t.

ft

Ascender of t is shorter than the ascender of f.

ft

✏ Circle your best **f** and **t**.

1 LOOK at your writing.

2 PLAN which letters need work. How will you make them look more like the models?

3 PRACTICE the letters that need more work.

GETTY-DUBAY BASIC ITALIC CAPITALS:
WIDE, MEDIUM and NARROW

Trace and copy.

WIDE

C

width
equals
height

C G O Q D M W

M and W slightly wider

C G O Q D M W

capital height

✎ Are your C, G, O, Q, and D wide? Yes___ No___

✎ Are your M and W slightly wider? Yes___ No___

PRACTICE letters here
and on lined paper.

NOTE: All capitals
start at top.

MEDIUM

width
is ⁴/₅
of height

THANKUVXYZ

THANKUVXYZ

HINT: To help
remember the medium
width letters they spell
"Thank U (you) V, X, Y,
and Z".

✎ Are your letters medium width? Yes___ No___

PRACTICE letters here
and on lined paper.

NOTE:
For Basic Italic Capital
assessment, see
INSTRUCTION MANUAL p.64.

Trace and copy.

NARROW

width
is 1/2
of height

E F L B P R S J I

E F L B P R S J I

✏ Are your letters narrow width?   Yes___ No___

PRACTICE letters here
and on lined paper.

REVIEW: BASIC ITALIC CAPITALS AND LOWERCASE

Aa Bb Cc Dd Ee Ff Gg

A

Hh Ii Jj Kk Ll Mm Nn

Oo Pp Qq Rr Ss Tt Uu

Vv Ww Xx Yy & Zz

1 LOOK at your writing.
Pick your best letters.

2 Pick the letters that
need work. Compare
them with the models.
PLAN how to make
them look more like
the models.

3 Place lined paper over
the models and trace.
PRACTICE on lined
paper.

NUMERALS: The size of numerals is one body height.

0 1 2 3 4 4 5 5 6 7 8 9 10 11 12

0

NOTE: For origins of numerals and more practice see page 52.

WORD ORIGINS

NOTE: Small capitals are used here. The capitals are the same height as the lowercase body height of 4mm.

ACRONYM: A word formed from the first letters or syllables of other words.

A

tip: to insure promptness

t

NOTE: SPACING BETWEEN LETTERS

in Two downstrokes are the farthest apart.

io A curve and a downstroke are a little closer.

ba Two curves are the closest, almost touching.

zip: zone improvement plan

z

In the 18th century, customers arriving at an inn would hand the waiter coins and a paper bearing the initials T. I. P.*

laser: light amplification by simulated emission of radiation

l

radar: radio detecting and ranging

r

NOTE: SPACING BETWEEN WORDS
Leave the width of n between words.

scuba: self-contained underwater breathing apparatus

s

INITIALIZATIONS: Initials used instead of words.

I

LOOK at your writing.

PLAN which letters need work.

PRACTICE those letters here and on lined paper.

RV: recreational vehicle

R

TLC: tender loving care

T

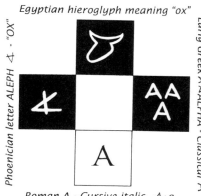

Egyptian hieroglyph meaning "ox"

Phoenician letter ALEPH ∢ - "OX"

Early Greek A ∧ ALPHA - Classical A

Roman A - Cursive italic A · a

*From AN ALMANAC OF WORDS AT PLAY, by Willard R. Espy.

GETTY-DUBAY CURSIVE ITALIC

Addition: descender for f
Options: dot or jot for i and j, two-stroke k or one-stroke k
Serifs: soft angle exit serits - a d h i k l u n m z
            soft angle entrance serifs - r n m x z
            sharp angle entrance serifs - j p v w

Improvement: shape

CURSIVE ITALIC LOWERCASE: 8 JOINS

Join 1. diagonal - an
Join 2. diagonal swing up - au
Join 3. diagonal start back - ao
Join 4. diagonal into e - ae
Join 5. horizontal - on
Join 6. diagonal out of r - ru
Join 7. horizontal to diagonal - sn
Join 8. diagonal to horizontal - aa
Lifts - lift before f and z; lift after g j q y
Review

Vowel sounds, consonant sounds, phonograms, prefixes, suffixes, letter
and envelope writing

Improvement: shape, size, spacing, slope

CURSIVE CAPITALS

Origins: Egyptian, Phoenician, Greek, Roman
Basic Italic and Cursive Italic
Writing practice using cities of the world

Improvement: shape, size, slope

READING LOOPED CURSIVE
Comparison of cursive italic handwriting with looped cursive handwriting

SLOPE, SPEED
Slope Guidelines
Timed Writing

LINES
5mm, 4mm

abcdefghijklmnopqrstuvwxyz

ADDITION & OPTIONS:

ADDITION:
f adds a descender

OPTION:
i and j use a dot or jot

OPTION: k may also be a
one-stroke letter

f · f   i · i or i   j · j or j   k · k or k

SERIFS: *Serifs are lines added to letters.*
There are exit serifs and entrance serifs.

Serifs are like hands
reaching out to join letters.

EXIT SERIF: *End with a soft angle at the baseline*
into a short diagonal. (n, m, and x also have entrance serifs.)

←diagonal
soft angle

AVOID a hook

AVOID a scoop

a · a a	d · d d
h · h h	i · i i
k · k k	l · l l
m · m m	n · n n
u · u u	x · x x

☐ 1
LOOK at your writing.
Pick your best letters.
Answer the question.

✏ Circle some of your best exit serifs.   Yes___ No___

✏ Are your letters ending with a soft angle exit serif?   Yes___ No___

☐ 2
Pick the letters that
need work. Compare
them with the models.
PLAN how to make
them look more like
the models.

☐ 3
PRACTICE here the
letters that need work.

ENTRANCE SERIFS:

There are two kinds of entrance serifs—soft angle entrance serifs and sharp angle entrance serifs.

SOFT ANGLE
ENTRANCE SERIF: *Begin with a short diagonal line to a soft angle. (**m**, **n**, and **x** have exit serifs also)*

soft angle

diagonal →

m · m · m   n · n · n

r · r · r   x · x · x

✎ Circle your best soft angle entrance serif.

SHARP ANGLE
ENTRANCE SERIF: *Begin with a short diagonal line to a sharp angle.*

sharp angle

diagonal →

j · j · j   p · p · p

v · v · v   w · w · w

✎ Circle your best sharp angle entrance serif.

PRACTICE the letters that need more work.

AVOID a scoop

CURSIVE Z: Add short entrance and exit serifs to z.   *z · z · z*

✎ Circle your best **z**.

REVIEW: CURSIVE ITALIC LOWERCASE LETTERS

No change: **b, c, e, g, o, q, s, t,** and **y.**

[1]   *a b c d e f g h i j k l m*
                                              or *k*

Trace and copy.
LOOK at your writing.

[2]   *a*

PLAN which letters need work.

[3]   *n o p q r s t u v w x y z*

PRACTICE those letters on lined paper.   *n*

GETTY-DUBAY CURSIVE ITALIC LOWERCASE JOINS OVERVIEW

JOIN 1: DIAGONAL *Join with a straight diagonal line.*

an   an an an an   an

Trace and copy.

Serifs are like hands reaching out to join letters.

in in in in   in

en en en   en

un un un un   un

NOTE:
For optional join into
n, m, r and x using
join 2, see pages 13,
14, and 24.

em   er   ex

em

im   ir   ix

LOOK at your writing.
Answer the question.

im

PLAN which joins
need work. How will
you make them look
more like the models?

um um   ur   ux

Are you using a straight diagonal line for the join?   Yes___ No___

PRACTICE the joins
that need more work.

JOIN 2: DIAGONAL SWING UP *Join with a straight diagonal line.*

au   au au au au   au

Serifs reach out to join letters.

ay   ai   at

ay   ai   at

Trace and copy. aj aj   ap ap

an an   aw aw

Serifs reach out to join letters with ascenders.

al al al al   a

imaginary branching line ah ah   ak ak   ab ab

el el   eh eh   eb eb   ek ek

✎ Are you joining at the imaginary branching line?   Yes____   No____

OPTION: Join into n, m, r, and x with Diagonal Swing Up.

an an   am am

ar ar   ax ax

en en   em em   er er   ex ex

JOIN 3: DIAGONAL START BACK   Join with a straight diagonal line.

Serifs reach up
to the waistline.

ao   ao ao ao ao

eo eo   io io   uo uo

✎ Are you joining into o with a straight diagonal line?   Yes____   No____

OPTION: Join into s from the baseline to the waistline,
leaving off the horizontal top of s.

as as   es es

is is   us us

OPTION: See Join 8 where the s shape is unchanged.

as as   es es   is is   us us

PRACTICE the joins
that need more work.

JOIN 4: DIAGONAL INTO e *Join with a diagonal line.*

ae *ae ae ae ae* *ae*

Trace and copy.

Join into e out of letters ending at the baseline.

ee ee ie ie ue ue

✏ *Are you joining into **e** at the branching line?* Yes____ No____

OPTION: Lift before e from baseline.

ae ae ee ee ie ie ue ue

JOIN 5: HORIZONTAL *Join with a horizontal line at the waistline.*

ou *ou ou ou ou* *ou*

Reach out along the waistline.

on on oo oo oa oa

tu tu tu Reach out from the crossbar.

fo fo fa fa

vi wi vi wi xi xi

✏ *Are you joining with a horizontal join out of **o, t, f, v,** and **x?*** Yes____ No____

OPTION: Join into e from crossbar at the waistline. *te te fe fe*

OPTION: Join into e out of the first stroke of t. *te te*

OPTION: Lift before e from waistline. *te te fe fe*

NOTE: When lifting between letters, be sure to keep letters close together.
Joins are natural spacers—when not using a join, keep letters close.

JOIN 6: DIAGONAL OUT OF r Join with a short diagonal line.

ru ru ru ru   ru

Trace and copy.

It's just a short reach out of r.

rn rn   ro ro   ra ra   re re

✎ Are you joining out of r with a short diagonal line? Yes____   No____

OPTION: Lift after r.

ru ru   rn rn   ro ro   ra ra

JOIN 7: HORIZONTAL TO DIAGONAL Join with a horizontal line blending into a diagonal line.

sn sn sn sn   sn

su su   so so   bo po

se   be   pe   Follow back out of s, b, and p.

se   be   pe

OPTION: Lift after s, b, and p.

sn sn   bo bo   po po   be be

JOIN 8: DIAGONAL TO HORIZONTAL Join with a diagonal line blending into a horizontal line.

aa aa aa aa   aa

ac ad ag aq as   Reach out to join into a, c, d, g, q, and s.

ac

OPTION: Lift before a, c, d, g, q, and s when joining from the baseline.

aa aa   ac ac   ad ad

LIFTS: Lift before f and lift before z from baseline. Lift after g, j, q, and y.

JOIN 1 | *an an an* | OPTION:

JOIN 2 | *au au*

JOIN 3 | *ao ao as* | OPTION:

JOIN 4 | *ae ae ae* | OPTION:

JOIN 5 | *on on*

JOIN 6 | *ru ru ru* | OPTION:

JOIN 7 | *sn sn sn* | OPTION:

JOIN 8 | *aa aa aa* | OPTION:

Body height is 5mm (previous body height was 6mm).

The letter *n* is used to show how to join into and out of letters.

NOTE: Basic italic capitals may be used with cursive italic lowercase if preferred to cursive capitals.

NOTE: For practice of cursive capitals see pages 45-49.

[1] LOOK at your writing. Pick your best letters.

[2] Pick the letters that need work. Compare them with the models PLAN how to make them look more like the models.

[3] PRACTICE the letters that need more work.

NOTE: For further practice of capitals see pages 45-49.

For Cursive Italic Capitals and Lowercase assessment see INSTRUCTION MANUAL pp. 65-66.

CURSIVE ITALIC CAPITALS AND LOWERCASE

A ana or *na*   *B bnb* or *bn*   *C cnc* or *nc*   *D dnd* or *nd*

E ene or *ne*   *F fnf*   *G gng* or *ng*   *H hnh*

I ini   *J jnj*   *K knk* or *knk*   *L lnl*

M mnm or *mnm*   *N nnn* or *nnn*   *O ono*   *P pnp* or *pn*

Q qnq or *nq*   *R rnr* or *rnr*   *S sns* or *sns*   *T tnt*

U unu   *V vnv*   *W wnw*   *X xnx* or *nx*

Y yny   *Z znz*

A quick brown fox jumps over the lazy dog. Aq

GETTY-DUBAY CURSIVE ITALIC LOWERCASE JOINS

JOIN 1: DIAGONAL

*Join 1 is a straight diagonal line from the baseline to the waistline into **n, m, r,** and **x**.*

an or an

diagonal
to soft angle

an | *an en in kn mn nn un*

Trace & copy. *an*

Double n
Silent n

nn running winner   n autumn
nn

PREFIX: en-
SUFFIX: -en

en- enclose encourage   -en taken
en

CONSONANT SOUND: KN: N sound

kn knot know or know
kn

PREFIX: in-

in- include interpret
in

PREFIX: un-

un- unusual
un

Egyptian hieroglyph "house"

Phoenician letter BETH 𐤁 "house"

Early Greek BETA - Classical B

Roman B - Cursive italic B · b

✏ Circle one of your best diagonal joins into **n**.

WORD ORIGINS

JOIN 1 joins are underlined.

CLIPPED WORDS are words shortened by common use, known as Zipf's Principle.
C

ZIPF'S PRINCIPLE: *The principle of least effort—George Kingsley Zipf, Professor of Comparative Philology at Harvard University. (Philology is the study of literature.)*

Write the shortened form of each word.

advertisement omnibus gymnasium
a
hamburger memorandum referee

Write other clipped words from automobile, bicycle, examination, mathematics, and veterinarian.

a̦ a̦m̂

diagonal
to soft angle

PREFIX: im-
Double m

am Trace & copy.

am em im mm um

am

im-improve   mm humming

im

a̦ a̦r̂

diagonal
to soft angle

VOWEL SOUNDS:
AR: AIR sound
AR: AR sound

ER: R sound
IR: R sound

UR: R sound

CONSONANT
SOUNDS:
CR: CR blend
DR: DR blend
SUFFIX: -er

ar Trace & copy.

ar er ir ur

ar

ar care   ar artist

ar

er water   ir circle

er

ur surface murmur

ur

cr create   dr dream   -er writer

cr

G added to alphabet 3rd cent. BC

Phoenician letter GIMEL ʌ "camel"

Early Greek ⋋ - GAMMA - Classical Γ

C

G

Roman C - Cursive italic C · c
Roman G - Cursive italic G · g

✏ Circle some of your best diagonal joins into **m** and into **r**.

WORD ORIGINS

JOIN 1 joins are
underlined.

ONOMATOPOEIA: Words borrowed from sounds. Onomatopoeic words resemble the real sound that they refer to, such as bang, buzz, crack, cuckoo, hiss, meow, murmur, slurp, and zip.

Write other
onomatopoeic words
here and on lined
paper.

a˺ ax̃

**diagonal
to soft angle**

CONSONANT SOUND:
X: KS sound
PREFIX: ex-

ax | ax ex ix ux ˜x˜ x

Trace & copy. ax

x next relax ex- exceed explore

ix

✎ Circle one of your best joins into x.

REVIEW: JOIN 1

WORD ORIGINS

JOIN 1 joins are
underlined.

□ 1

LOOK at your
writing. Circle some
of your best diagonal
joins. Are you using a
straight line for your
diagonal join?
Yes ___ No___

Pick the joins that
need work. Compare
them with the
models. **PLAN** how to
make the joins look
more like the models.

□ 3

PRACTICE those joins
here and on lined
paper.

COMPOUND WORDS are words glued
together to form new words, such as
birthday, copyright, homemade,
notebook, pancake, and watercolor.
C

CONTRACTIONS are words formed by
substituting an apostrophe for a letter
or letters, such as I'll (I will), I'm (I am),
you're (you are), and we're (we are).
C

OPTION: Join into n, m, r, and x with Diagonal Swing Up.

NOTE:
For optional join
into n, m, r, and
x using Join 2
see page. 24.

an am ar ax · en em er ex

an

in im ir ix · un um ur ux

in

Phoenician letter DALETH "door"

Egyptian hieroglyph meaning "door"

Early Greek ◁D- DELTA - Classical Δ

D

Roman D - Cursive italic D · d

JOIN 2: DIAGONAL SWING UP

Join 2 is a straight diagonal line from the baseline to the branching line, then a swing up to the waistline or ascender height into **b, h, i, j, k, l, p, t, u, v, w,** and **y**. Optional join into n, m, r, and x.

a, au
diagonal swing up

VOWEL SOUND:
AU: broad O

au

Trace & copy.

au eu iu lu mu nu

au

au author because launch caution

au

a, ay
diagonal swing up

VOWEL SOUND:
AY: long A
SUFFIXES: -cy, -ly, -y

ay

ay cy ey iy ly my ny uy

ay

ay always today -cy accuracy

ay

-ly slowly neatly -y rainy sunny

uy

✎ Circle some of your best diagonal swing up joins into **u** and into **y**.

WORD ORIGINS

JOIN 2 joins are underlined.

PORTMANTEAU WORDS are words that have been blended together, such as brunch (breakfast + lunch), modem (modulator + demodulator), smog (smoke + fog), and twirl (twist + whirl).

Write other portmanteau words here and on lined paper.

a͢ ai
diagonal swing up

ai | ai ci di ei hi ki li mi ni ui

Trace & copy. | ai

VOWEL SOUND:
AI: long A

ai aim detail

ai

a͢ aj
a͢ ap
diagonal swing up

aj ap | aj ap ej ep

aj

Egyptian hieroglyph "behold"

Phoenician letter HE - "look," "behold"

Early Greek EPSILON ꟻ Classical E

Roman E - Cursive italic E · e

✐ Circle your best joins into **i**, **p**, and **j**.

WORD ORIGINS

JOIN 2 joins are underlined.

Fabric of Nimes, France

Samuel Maverick, a Texan who didn't brand his cattle

Louis Pasteur, French bacteriologist

Alessandro Volta, Italian physicist

James Watt, Scottish engineer and inventor

Write words from names.

WORDS FROM NAMES: Words borrowed from names of people & places include denim – serge de Nimes, maverick – Samuel Maverick, or ck pasteurize – Louis Pasteur, tangerine – Tangier, Morocco, volt – Alessandro Volta, and watt – James Watt.

a

Copy on lined paper.

NOTE: Ampersand is a short form of "and." It combines the letters **e** and **t**, the Latin word "et" meaning "and."

ET &

NOTE: The Hawaiian alphabet has twelve letters: a, e, h, i, k, l, m, n, o, p, u, and w.

WORDS FROM OTHER LANGUAGES: Words borrowed from foreign words & phrases include et cetera – and others (Latin), vice versa – conversely (Latin), and résumé – summary (French). aloha – hello/goodbye (Hawaiian)

a⟋ at
**diagonal
swing up**

SUFFIX: -ant
Double t

REMINDER: **t** has a
short ascender.

at   at et it ut tt tt tt   large U shape   long crossbar

Trace & copy.   at

-ant assistant   tt written or written

ant

✎ Does your **t** have a short ascender?

Yes ____   No ____

a⟋ al
**diagonal
swing up**

VOWEL SOUND:
AL: broad O
CONSONANT SOUND:
CL: CL blend

SUFFIXES: -al, -ily

al   al el il ll ul

al

al altogether   cl clever include

al

-al natural -ily happily speedily

al

meaning "hook," "nail" - Early Greek

Phoenician letter VAU   Y

ꟻF   DIGAMMA   ꟻ·F or Ⅎ·F

F

Roman F - Cursive italic F · f

✎ Circle some of your best diagonal swing-up joins into **t** and into **l**.

WORD ORIGINS

JOIN 2 joins are
underlined.

Etymology is the
study of word origins.
Greek and Latin roots
unlock the meaning
of many English
words.

at

NOTE: Join into **l** at
the branching line.

al AVOID
scoop and loop

GREEK AND LATIN ROOTS are found in
many words. Greek roots include
scop (see) in microscope, graph (write)
in autograph, and photo (light) in
photograph.

G

Latin roots include man (hand) in
manual, scribe-script (write) in
describe, & sign (mark) in signature.

a, a'h
**diagonal
swing up**

ah ab ak | ah ab ak eh eb ek

ah

Trace & copy.

**CONSONANT SOUND:
CH: digraph
Silent h, b, & k**

ch children h honest b lamb k know

ch

✎ Circle some of your best diagonal swing-up joins into **h**, **b**, and **k**.

**JOIN 2 joins are
underlined.**

HOMOPHONES are words that sound the
same but have different meanings and
different spellings.

H

bite, byte, bight byte: computer data unit
bight: slack part of rope · blue, blew
isle, aisle, I'll · scent, sent, cent
sew, so, sow · there, their, they're

**Copy the
homophones above
or write other
homophones here
and on lined paper.
(There are over 300!)**

**Complete each
homophone by
writing the missing
word or words.**

ate,   · be,   · cell,
doe,   · fare,   · for,
hare,   · heel,   · hour,
it's,   · knot,   · know,
lone,   · Maine,   ,
meet,   · oar,   · pause,
rap,   · right,   · sail,
tale,   · to,   , · where,
would,   · you're,

Answers on page 24.

av AW

diagonal swing up

av aw — *av aw ev ew iv iw uv uw*

Trace & copy.

av

VOWEL SOUND:
AW: broad O

aw awe draw lawn

aw

OPTION: v and w may be written with either a sharp angle or a soft angle at the baseline.

av aw ev ew iv iw

av

🖉 Circle your best join into **v** and **w**.

meaning "fence" - Early Greek ETA

Phoenician letter CHETH

B · H · Classical letter H

Roman H - Cursive italic H · h

JOIN 1 joins are underlined.

HOMOGRAPHS *are words that are spelled the same but have different meanings and different origins, such as tip, tip, & tip.*

tip: end point
tip: slant
tip: present of money for services

H

Think of different meanings of these words.

bank, bow, can, date, fast, fine, fly, gum, hide, jet, lap, like, mean, pen, pole, prune, rest, row, scale, seal, slip, sow, squash, tap, tear, top, well, yard

Copy the homographs or write others here and on lined paper. (There are over 300!)

OPTION: Join into n, m, r, and x with Diagonal Swing Up

Join at the imaginary branching line.

→ *an en in un am em im um*

→ *an*

ar er ir ur ax ex ix ux

ar

Homophone answers are: eight, bee, sell, dough, fair, four, hair, heal, our, its, not, no, loan, main & mane, meat, or, paws, wrap, write, sale, tail, too & two, wear, wood, your.

an   in   am   minimum

REVIEW: JOIN 2

JOIN 2 joins are underlined.

1

LOOK at your writing. Circle some of your best diagonal swing up joins. Are you joining at the imaginary branching line?
Yes ___ No ___
Are you AVOIDING a "scoop and loop" when joining into letters with ascenders?
Yes ___ No ___

2

Pick the joins that need work. Compare them with the models. PLAN how to make them look more like the models.

3

PRACTICE those joins here and on lined paper.

SYNONYMS *are words that have similar meanings, such as have, own, possess; help, aid, assist; and one, single, unit.*

S

ANTONYMS *are words that mean the opposite or nearly the opposite of each other, such as to-from, sound-silence, answer-question, or problem-solution.*

A

WORD GROUPS

ANALOGIES *show a likeness in some way between things otherwise unlike.*

A

Bird is to sky as fish is to sea. (place)

B

Determine the relationship between two words, then find other pairs of words that have a similar relationship, such as **in : out :: hot : cold** (opposites).
Write the missing word in the following analogies.

Relationships are:

antonyms

synonyms

purpose

action to object

characteristics

whole-part

place

left : right :: top :

easy : simple :: hard :

chair : sit :: bed :

talk : mouth :: hear :

snow : cold :: sun :

book : character :: recipe :

library : books :: cupboard :

Answers are on page 26.

JOIN 3: DIAGONAL START BACK

Join 3 is a straight diagonal line from the baseline to the waistline. From there start back into **o**.

a/ ao
diagonal
start back

ao ao co do eo ho io ko uo

Trace & copy. ao

Egyptian hieroglyph ⟿ for "hand"

VOWEL SOUND:
O: long O

o open poem piano

o

VOWEL SOUND:
O: short O
PREFIX: co-

o opposite co-cooperate

o

✏ Circle one of your best diagonal joins into o.

OPTION: Join into s from the baseline to the waistline, leaving off the horizontal top of s.

a/ a's
CONSONANT SOUND:
S: regular
PREFIX: dis-

as as   is is   es es   us

s question answer   dis-displaced

s

CONSONANT SOUND:
S: Z sound
PREFIX: mis-

s music please mis-misplaced

s

OPTION: See Join 8 where the s shape is unchanged.

as es is us ss   music please

as

✏ Circle one of your best diagonal joins into s.

WORD GROUPS

WORD IDIOMS are formed around key
words, such as GO—go all out, go easy,
go far, go for it, go into, go on, go out,
go with, & go without.

JOIN 3 joins are
underlined.

W

Other key words are
blow, fall, hang, hit,
keep, put, run, see,
sit, take, and turn.

Answers to completed
analogies are: bottom,
difficult, sleep, ear, hot,
ingredient, dishes.

Phoenician letter YOD ⦚ "hand" • *Roman I*

Early Greek IOTA ⟨·⟩ · Classical I · ΙΩΤΑ Γ

| ⟿ |
2		⟩⟩
	I
	J

Cursive italic I·i J·j   Middle Ages

REVIEW: JOIN 3

WORD GROUPS

JOIN 3 joins are underlined.

A SIMILE *is* a figure of speech that *uses* the words "*as*" or "*like*."

as busy as a bee · as happy as a clam

LIKE poem by David Greenberg

A pair of scissors is like a bird.
A book is like a garden in the pocket.

Metaphors are phrases used as adverbs or adjectives to describe persons, places, things, and actions; not to be taken literally, but to be enjoyed.

A METAPHOR *is* a figure of speech that *compares* two things but *does not use* the words "*like*" or "*as*."

in the evening of life
the ship plows the sea
a mountain of paperwork

1

LOOK at your writing. Circle some of your best diagonal joins into o and s. Are you joining with a straight diagonal line? Yes___ No___

2

PLAN how to make the joins that need more work look more like the models.

3

PRACTICE the joins that need more work using the lines here and lined paper.

JOIN 2: DIAGONAL INTO e

Join 4 is a straight diagonal line to the branching line into the center of e.

a → ae
diagonal
into e

ae | ae ce de ee he ie le me ne ue

Trace & copy. | ae

VOWEL SOUND:
E: long E

e equal me he she
e

VOWEL SOUND:
EE: long E

OPTIONAL JOIN ✱

ee seem or seem agree
ee

VOWEL SOUND:
E: short E

e enjoy help next
e

VOWEL SOUND:
E: silent

e write homework
e

SUFFIX: -ment

-ment compliment development
ment

✱REMINDER: You may
join into m, n, r, and
x using Join 2.

Egyptian hieroglyph ⬳ "palm"

Phoenician letter KAPPA - "palm"

Early Greek KAPPA ϡ · k · Classical k

Roman K - Cursive italic K · k

✎ Circle some of your best diagonal joins into e.

OPTION: Lift before e from baseline.

ae ce de ee he ie le me ne ue
ae

NOTE: When lifting between letters be sure to keep letters close together.
Joins are natural spacers -- when not using a join keep letters close.

WORD GROUPS

NOTE:
Join into e at the
branching line.

ae imaginary
branching line

AVOID
scoop and loop.

ae
↑
scoop

NOTE: For two-stroke e see
INSTRUCTION MANUAL.

IDIOMATIC EXPRESSIONS cannot be
understood from their literal meanings.

It's raining cats and dogs.
You have a green thumb.

REVIEW: JOIN 4

WORD GROUPS

JOIN 4 joins are underlined.

PROVERBS are common, wise or thoughtful sayings. P

REMINDER: You may prefer to use Join 2 to join into **n, m, r,** and **x.** From line 5 on, this join is used. Try it as an option.

A picture is worth a thousand words.
A penny saved is a penny earned.
The grass is always greener on the other side of the fence.
A

①

LOOK at your writing. Circle some of your best joins into **e.** Are you using a straight diagonal line joining into **e?**
Yes ___ No ___ .
Are you AVOIDING a "scoop and loop?"
Yes ___ No ___

A MAXIM is a general truth or rule of conduct. A

New England maxim

②

Pick the joins that need work. Compare them with the models. PLAN how to make the joins look more like the models.

Use it up, wear it out,
make it do, or do without.
U

Egyptian hieroglyph "ox-goad"

Phoenician letter LAMED ᒪ "cudgel"

Early Greek LAMBDA ᒪ or ᒐ · Classical ∧

I hear and I forget.
I see and I remember.
I do and I understand.

NOTE: **E** is our most used letter. Take care joining into **e.**

Roman L - Cursive italic L · l

Write this Chinese proverb on lined paper.

Give a man a fish,
and you feed him for a day.
Teach a man to fish
and you feed him for a lifetime.

③

PRACTICE on lined paper.

JOIN 5: HORIZONTAL

*Join 5 is a horizontal join at the waistline. Join out of **o**, **t**, **f**, **v**, **w**, and **x** into every letter, except **f**.*

σ⃗ *on*
horizontal

on | on or ou oy oi ow oo oa os

Trace & copy. | on

VOWEL SOUNDS:
OR: OR sound
OU: OU diphthong

or orchestra horn ou mountain
or

VOWEL SOUNDS:
OY: OI diphthong
OI: OI diphthong

oy voyage enjoy oi oil choice noise
oy

VOWEL SOUNDS:
OW: OU diphthong
OW: long O

ow vowel power ow throw snowball
ow

PREFIXES: com-, con-

com- combine comfort con- concert
com

SUFFIXES: -dom, -or

-dom freedom -or actor
dom

SUFFIXES: -ion, -ous

-ion action -ous joyous
ion

SUFFIX: -ious

-ious delicious
ious

Egyptian hieroglyph for "water"

Phoenician letter MEM - "water"

Early Greek MU ᴡ·ᴎ·Classical ᴍ

Roman M - Cursive italic ℳ·𝓂

✏ Circle some of your best horizontal joins out of **o**.

WORD GROUPS

JOIN 5 joins are underlined.

IMAGERY creates strong pictures or images in the reader's mind.

A blanket of soft snow covered the sleeping tractor. A

VOWEL SOUND:
OO: short OO

oo look notebook

oo

VOWEL SOUND:
OO: long OO

oo loose kangaroo

oo

VOWEL SOUND:
OA: long O

oa road goal approach

oa

SUFFIX: -ology

-ology word family uses
the suffix which means
"the science of" or "the study of," such as
Biology, Ecology, Geology, Meteorology,
Psychology, Sociology, and Zoology.

o

o   ot   ol

horizontal
swing up

Egyptian hieroglyph for "fish"

Phoenician letter NUN for "fish"

Early Greek NU - Classical N

Roman N - Cursive italic N n

OPTION: Join into e from waistline.

oe oe foe f   toe t   woe w

OPTION: Lift before e from waistline.

oe oe foe f   toe t   woe w

NOTE: When lifting between letters be sure to keep letters close together.
Joins are natural spacers -- when not using a join maintain the closeness of letters.

WORD GROUPS

HYPERBOLE is a statement exaggerated
fancifully for effect. H

JOIN 5 joins are
underlined.

The word "hyperbole"
comes from Greek
words: hyper = over,
above + ballein = to
throw.

That book weighs a ton.
I could sleep for a year.

Write these sayings
or other examples of
hyperbole.

t⃗ t⃗r
horizontal
out of crossbar

tr

Trace & copy.

tr tu ty ti tw to ta tl th tt

tr

CONSONANT
SOUNDS:
TR: TR blend
TW: TW blend

tr tree country tw twilight between

tr

PREFIX: auto-
SUFFIX: -tion

auto- autograph -tion direction

auto

SUFFIX: -ity

-ity diversity unity

ity

CONSONANT SOUND:
TH: digraph voiceless

th thank truth

th

CONSONANT SOUND:
TH: digraph voiced

th the then there

th

Egyptian hieroglyph ⬯ for "eye"

Phoenician letter AYIN · O · "eye"

Early Greek · Classical OMICRON

Roman O · Cursive italic O · o

🖉 Circle one of your best joins out of **t**.

OPTION: Join into e from crossbar at the waistline.

PREFIX: tele-
SUFFIX: -ite

te ten tele- telephone -ite favorite

te

OPTION: Lift before e from waistline.

te ten tele- telephone -ite favorite

te

NOTE: When lifting between letters, be sure to keep letters close together.
Joins are natural spacers—when not using a join, keep letters close.

OPTION: Join into e out of the first stroke of t.

te ten tele- telephone -ite favorite

te

🖉 Circle the option (lift or join) that is comfortable for you.

PRACTICE here and
on lined paper.

horizontal
out of crossbar

fr | fr fy fi fo fa fs fl ft ft ff

Trace & copy. fr

CONSONANT SOUNDS:
FR: FR blend
FL: FL blend

fr *friend carefree* fl *fluffy snowflake*

fr

SUFFIX: -ful

-ful *careful thoughtful successful*

ful

SUFFIX: -fy

-fy *identify satisfy*

fy

NOTE: Join **f** and **t**
with one crossbar.

ft *lift soft drift*

ft

🖊 Circle one of your best joins out of **f**.

OPTION: Join into e from crossbar at the waistline.

fe fe   few   fell

OPTION: Lift before e from waistline.

fe fe   few   fell

✏ Circle the option (lift or join) that is comfortable for you.

Egyptian hieroglyph ⌣ *"mouth"*

Phoenician letter PE ? *"mouth"*

Early Greek PI - ? *- Classical* Π

P

Roman P - Cursive italic P · p

WORD GROUPS

JOIN 5 joins are
underlined.

A EUPHEMISM is a mild or indirect
expression instead of one that is harsh
or unpleasantly direct.
A

passed away or crossed over (died)
canine control officer (dogcatcher)

REMINDER:
Relax. Hold your
pencil lightly, without
pinching.

horizontal

diagonal into e

CONSONANT SOUNDS:
WH: digraph (HW blend)
WR: R sound

vn wn   vn wn vi wi wi ve we

Trace & copy.

wh what why whiz   wr wrist writing
wn

SUFFIX: -ive

-ive active passive
ive

✏ Circle one of your best joins out of **v** and **w**.

QOPH "knot" - Early Greek KOPPA Φ

Phoenician letter Φ

Φ

Q

φ

- not in Classical Greek

Roman Q - Cursive italic Q·q

horizontal

diagonal into e

xu   xu xy xi xe

CONSONANT SOUND:
X: KS sound
PREFIX: ex-

x expert mixture   ex- exclaim
x

✏ Circle one of your best joins out of **x**.

OPTION: Lift before e from waistline.

ve ve   we we   xe xe

NOTE: When lifting between letters be sure to keep letters close together.
Joins are natural spacers -- when not using a join maintain the closeness of letters.

WORD GROUPS

JOIN 5 joins are underlined.

An OXYMORON is a combination of
contradictory or incongruous words.
-A

bittersweet · blacklight · freezer burn
clearly confused · jumbo shrimp
r

Write oxymora
(plural of oxymoron)
that you have heard.

REVIEW: JOIN 5

JOIN 5 joins are underlined.

[box 1]

LOOK at your writing. Circle some of your best joins out of **o, t, f, v, w,** and **x.**

[box 2]

PLAN how to make your joins look more like the models. Option: You may prefer to lift before joining into ascenders; if you do, be sure letters are close together.

[box 3]

PRACTICE on lined paper.

ALLITERATION is the repetition of a sound at the beginning of two or more neighboring words, such as wild and wooly, babbling brook, or pickled peppers.

A

WORD ENTERTAINMENT: TONGUE TWISTERS

six thick thistle sticks

rubber baby buggy bumpers

Which wristwatches are Swiss wristwatches?

LETTER SHAPE OPTIONS: Italic letter shapes are based on an elliptical shape which may be standard, expanded or compressed. Try the options and find which is comfortable for you.

STANDARD SHAPE — Peter Piper picked a peck of pickled

EXPANDED SHAPE — peppers. If Peter Piper picked a

COMPRESSED SHAPE — peck of pickled peppers, how many pecks of

STANDARD SHAPE — pickled peppers did Peter Piper pick?

Write on this line using your most comfortable letter shape.
NOTE: Whichever letter shape you prefer, be consistent.
AVOID uneven writing.

AVOID uneven

Which letter shape do you find most comfortable?

___expanded ___slightly expanded ___standard ___slightly compressed ___compressed

See Shape Guidelines, INSTRUCTION MANUAL, page 57.

JOIN 6: DIAGONAL OUT OF r

Join 6 is a short diagonal line out of r into all lettes, except f.

r ŕ rn
diagonal

rn rn ra re ri ro ru ry rr

Trace & copy. rn

CONSONANT SOUND:
R: regular
Double r
PREFIX: re-

r read your story rr error re-redo

r

SUFFIXES: -ry, -ery, -ern, - ary, - orium, -ory, -arium, -ure, -ward

-ry poetry -ery pottery -ern eastern

ry

rn rn

NOTE: Bend arm of r at the waistline before joining.

-ary library -orium auditorium

ary

-ory laboratory -arium aquarium

ory

AVOID rn looking like **m.** rn rn

AVOID r looking like **v.** v

-ure treasure -ward forward backward

ure

Take care joining out of r. Take your time. Legibility is most important.

Circle some of your best joins out of r.

OPTION: Lift after r. rn rn   ra ra   re re   ri ri

NOTE: When lifting after r, keep letters close together.

ro ro   ru ru   ry ry   rr rr

A RHOPALIC SENTENCE is a snowballing line in which each successive word has one more letter (or syllable) than the last.

JOIN 6 joins are underlined.

A

Rhopalic comes from "rhopalon"—Greek word for a type of club which thickens from the handle to the head.

Write your own rhopalic sentence on lined paper. Have words increase by one letter or one syllable.

I do not know where family doctors acquired illegibly perplexing handwriting.

First part of a twenty word rhopalic sentence from "Language On Vacation" by Dmitri A. Borgmann.

Egyptian hieroglyph for "head"

Phoenician letter RESH "head"

Early Greek RHO ⊲ ᛈ - Classical P

R

Roman R - Cursive italic R · r

REVIEW: JOIN 6

JOIN 6 joins are underlined.

□1

LOOK at your writing. Circle some of your best joins out of *r*. Are you bending the arm of *r* at the waistline so it reads as an *r*?
Yes____ No____

□2

PLAN what you need to do to make *r* more legible. You may need to use a pointed *r* to make it more legible.

□3 PRACTICE

Mnemonic to help remember the direction of annual time changes between Standard Time and Daylight Savings Time.

MNEMONIC DEVICES are a way to improve or develop the memory.

M

I before E, except after C, or when sounded like A as in "neighbor" or "weigh."

Spring forward, fall back.

Egyptian hieroglyphs ⌣ ⌣ "tooth"

Phoenician letter SHIN - "tooth"

Early Greek SIGMA ⌇⌇ - Classical Σ

W S

Roman S - Cursive italic S - s

LETTER SIZE OPTIONS

Each person has a comfortable letter size. This book has 6mm, 5mm, and 4mm body heights. Try the options and find which is comfortable for you.

5mm — Thirty days has September,

4.5mm — April, June, and November;

4mm — All the rest have thirty-one,

3.5mm — Excepting February alone,

3mm — Which has just four and twenty-four,

2.5mm — And every leap year one day more.

NOTE: Whichever letter size you choose, be consistent. AVOID uneven writing.
AVOID uneven

Write on a baseline only (no waistline) to find your comfortable letter height.

Which notebook paper size is best for you?

notebook paper | 9mm

7.5mm | notebook paper

WIDE-RULED NOTEBOOK PAPER
4.5mm body height or less

COLLEGE RULED NOTEBOOK PAPER
3.75mm body height or less

JOIN 7: HORIZONTAL TO DIAGONAL

*Join 7 is a horizontal line out of **b**, **p**, and **s** at the baseline blending into a diagonal line. Follow back out of **b**, **p**, and **s** joining into all letters, except **f** & **z**.*

s *sn*

→
horizontal
to diagonal

sn   *sn se si so su ss st sl sh sk*

Trace & copy. *sn*

CONSONANT
SOUNDS:
SN: SN blend
SM: SM blend

sn snowy sm smooth
sn

SP: SP blend
SW: SW blend

sp special sw swell
sp

ST: ST blend
SL: SL blend

st step sl slope
st

SH: digraph
SK: SK blend

sh shape sk skill
sh

SUFFIXES: -less, -est,
-ist, -wise, -ship

-less careless -est neatest -ist artist
less

-wise clockwise -ship friendship kinship
wise

Egyptian hieroglyph ☦ "mark"

Phoenician letter TAU "mark" "sign"

Early Greek TAU · T·T · Classical T

Roman T - Cursive italic *T·t*

b *bn pn*

→
horizontal
to diagonal

br pr   *br pr be pe bi pi bu pu*
br

CONSONANT SOUNDS:
BR: BR blend
BL: BL blend
PR: PR blend
PL: PL blend

Double s, b, & p

br bright bl blue pr print pl please
br

ss session bb bubble pp pepper
ss

✎ Circle some of your best joins out of **b**, **p**, and **s**.

OPTION: Lift after **s**, **b**, and **p**.   *sn sn   st st   ss ss*
br pr br pr   bb pp bb pp

NOTE: When lifting between letters be sure to keep letters close together.

REVIEW: JOIN 7

JOIN 7 joins are underlined.

1 LOOK at your writing. Circle one of your best horizontal to diagonal joins out of **b**, **p**, and **s**. Are you following back out of **b**, **p**, and **s**? Yes___ No___

2 PLAN what you need to do to make this join more like the models. Option: You may prefer to lift; if you do, be sure letters are close together.

3 PRACTICE on lined paper.

A PANGRAM is a verse, sentence, or phrase containing all the letters of the alphabet.

A

Quick wafting zephyrs vex bold Jim.

A quick brown fox jumps over the lazy dog.
A

"hook" "nail" - Y · Early Greek ꓥ·ꓶ

Phoenician letter VAU · U introduced in Middle

or F·F DIGAMMA - later dropped · 11th century

| Y | ꓶꓶ |

| V |
| u |
| W |

Ages · Roman V - W added in the Cursive italic U u · Vv · Ww

LETTER SLOPE OPTIONS: The models are written at a 5° slope. Italic handwriting may be written at any slope between 0° and 15°. Each person has a comfortable letter slope. Try the options and find which is comfortable for you.

NOTE: Whichever letter slope you prefer, be consistent. AVOID unven letter slope.

AVOID *uneven*

As we write we all vary slightly from our chosen slope. We are not machines! An overall even letter slope is the goal.

If your slope is uneven, see Slope Guidelines, page 44.

0° Autumn was quiet except for
A

5° the crunch of golden brown leaves

10° dizzy from their journey back to earth.

15° Autumn was quiet except for the crunch

Write on this line using your most comfortable letter slope. Circle the letter slope number that you prefer.

| 0° | 1° – 4° | 5° | 6° – 9° | 10° | 11° – 14° | 15° |

JOIN 8: DIAGONAL TO HORIZONTAL

*Join 8 is a diagonal line from the baseline blending into a horizontal line at the waistine, joining into **a**, **c**, **d**, **g**, **q**, and **s**.*

a/ aa̓
**diagonal
to horizontal**

aa ad

aa ad ea ed ia id ua ud

Trace & copy.

aa

VOWEL SOUNDS:
EA: long E
EA: short E
(read, present tense=long e;
read, past tense= short e)

ea easily read ea pleasant meadow

ea

**SUFFIXES: -ian, -ed,
-ade, -ular**

-ian musician -ed listened learned

ian

-ade parade -ular circular regular

ade

✏ Circle one of your best joins into **a** and **d**.

SAMEKH - "prop" • Early Greek Ⱶ ·x

Phoenician letter Ⱶ

Ⱶ

X

Ⱶ X
Ⱶ

changed to XI - Classical Ⱶ

Roman X - Cursive italic X x

a/ ac̓
**diagonal
to horizontal**

ac

ac ec ic uc

uc

CONSONANT SOUND:
SC: SC blend
SUFFIX: -ic

sc describe -ic poetic comic

sc

✏ Circle one of your best joins into **c**.

**JOIN 8 joins are
underlined.**

An ANAGRAM is a word or phrase made
out of another by changing the order of
the letters. (stop, tops, opts, post, pots, spot)

A

**Write four words
using the letters in
"pears" and three
words using the
letters in "smile."**

pears (4)

smile (3)

Answers on page 42.

a ag aq

ag aq ag aq eg eq ig iq ug uq

diagonal
to horizontal

Trace & copy. ag

CONSONANT SOUNDS:
NG: NG
Q: KW sound

ng strong young q equal inquire

ng

SUFFIXES: -ing, -age

-ing talking writing -age voyage

ing

Circle one of your best joins into g and q.

"hook" "nail" - Early Greek UPSILON

Phoenician letter VAU

Y & Classical Greek Y

Roman Y - Cursive italic *y y*

a as

as as es is us ss

diagonal
to horizontal

as

SUFFIXES: -ics, -ness

-ics physics politics -ness kindness

NOTE: AVOID wave

is

ics

Circle one of your best joins into s.

OPTION: Lift before a, c, d, g, q, and s when joining from the baseline.

aa aa ac ac ad ad ag ag

aq aq as as ea ea ed ed

NOTE: When lifting between letters be sure to keep letters close together.

JOIN 8 joins are
underlined.

A PUN is a play on words of the same
sound but different meanings or on
different uses of a word for a witty effect.
A

Tom Swifties:

SPEED: After all the
joins are learned,
begin to increase
your speed of writing.
Do the Timed Writing
on page 44. Repeat.
Always maintain
legibility.

"My bicycle wheel is melting," Tom
spoke softly.
"It's a mongrel," said Tom muttering.
"Chocolate, not vanilla!" I screamed.

REVIEW: JOIN 8

JOIN 8 joins are underlined.

1 LOOK at your writing.

2 PLAN how to make the joins look more like the models.

3 PRACTICE on lined paper.

A PALINDROME is a word, phrase, verse, or sentence that reads the same forward as backward.

Palindromic words

Hannah, Otto, Mom, Dad, kayak, & radar.

Palindromic sentences

Never odd or even. N

Madam, I'm Adam. M

A man, a plan, a canal, Panama!

LETTER SPACING OPTIONS: The models above are written with standard spacing. Other options are expanded spacing and compressed spacing. Try the options and find which is comfortable for you.

Palindrome using words instead of letters.
EXPANDED SPACING

You can cage a swallow, can't you

COMPRESSED SPACING

but you can't swallow a cage, can you?

Write on this line using your most comfortable letter spacing. Whichever letter spacing you prefer, be consistent. AVOID uneven spacing.
AVOID *uneven*

✏ Circle the letter spacing that is most comfortable for you.

Standard   Expanded   Compressed

WORDS THAT READ DIFFERENTLY BACKWARD & FORWARD
Write these words backward. Write other words, such as peek, slap, reed, sleep, and strap.

now, reward, spot

stop, strap, straw

See Spacing Guidelines, INSTRUCTION MANUAL, page 57.

Answers to anagram on page 40:
pears, spear, reaps, pares, spare; smile, miles, limes, slime.

Egyptian hieroglyph for "weapon"

Phoenician letter ZAYIN "weapon"

Early Greek ZETA - 1 - Classical Z

Roman Z - Cursive italic Z z

LIFTS: Lift before f and lift before z from baseline. Lift after g, j, q, and y.

When letters are not joined, place letters close together; AVOID gap.

af az af az ef ez if iz of oz

Trace & copy.

_af_

ga ju qu yu ga ju qu yu

_ga_

CONSONANT SOUND:
F: regular
Z: regular
Double f, z, g

f family z size ff off zz pizza gg egg

f

CONSONANT SOUNDS:
GH: silent
GL: GL blend
GR: GR blend

gh neighbor gl glimpse gr agree

g

CONSONANT SOUNDS:
J: regular
Q: KW sound
Y: consonant
Y: long E
Y: long I

j enjoy q question y you y very y my

j

Are you AVOIDING a gap when lifting between letters in a word? Yes___ No___

NOTE: When lifting between letters, be sure to keep letters close together.
Joins are natural spacers—when not using a join, keep letters close.

A REBUS is a riddle composed of pictures,
letters and/or numerals that represent
a word, phrase, or sentence.

Copy on lined paper.

Write the answers to these rebuses.

onalle—

U R Y Y 4 ME—

ME
AL —

paid —
he

FANNIE DOOLEY RIDDLE: Why does Fannie Dooley like pizza, but not fries? Why does she like eggs, but doesn't like chickens? Does she prefer off or on?

Answers on page 51.

Fannie Dooley likes pizza & dislikes fries.
Fannie Dooley likes eggs, but not chickens.

T —

SLOPE GUIDELINES:

A 5° letter slope is used for basic and cursive.

OPTIONS: *You have a choice of slope--from a vertical of 0° to a slope of 15°.*
This is the choice range:

Which is your most comfortable letter slope? Whichever letter slope you choose, use that slope for all your writing.

LOOK at your writing.

 Do you have an even letter slope?
Yes___ No___

SLOPE GUIDE:

Make your own slope guide to fit your choice of letter slope. Place a sheet of notebook paper at an angle under your writing paper and line up the lines with your letter slope.

 Do your letters have different slopes?
Yes___ No___

PLAN how to write with an even letter slope. Use the following exercise to find a comfortable slope for you.

1. write word
2. draw slope lines over letters
3. pick one slope
4. draw parallel lines
5. write over slope lines

Choose a letter slope and write all your letters using that slope.

Use paper clips or removable tape to hold the two sheets together. On the undersheet outline the edge of the writing paper so you know where to place the next sheet of paper.

0°   5°   10°   15°

SPEED: TIMED WRITING *Use the timed writing to help increase speed.*

The goal is to increase the number of words written per minute.
Begin by writing the following sentence (or another sentence) as a warm-up.

A quick brown fox jumps over the lazy dog.

1. TIME LENGTH: 1 MINUTE *Write the sentence at your most comfortable speed. If you finish before the time is up, begin the sentence again. Count the number of words written. Write this number in the margin.*

2. TIME LENGTH: 1 MINUTE *Write the sentence a little faster. Try to add one or two more words to your total. Count the number of words written.*

3. TIME LENGTH: 1 MINUTE *Write the sentence as fast as you can. Count the number of words written.*

4. TIME LENGTH: 1 MINUTE *Write the sentence at a comfortable speed. Count the number of words written. Write the number in the margin.*

Repeat process once a month.   *Compare the total of # 4 to # 1.*
Did you increase the number of words written by one or more? Yes___ No___

EYES CLOSED   *Using the same sentence, do this exercise as a follow-up to the timed writing. Use a non-lined sheet of paper. Close your eyes. Picture in your mind's eye the shape of each letter as you write. Take all the time you need.*
You may be amazed how well you can write with your eyes closed.

See Speed Guidelines.
INSTRUCTIONAL MANUAL pages 60, 61

GETTY-DUBAY BASIC ITALIC & CURSIVE ITALIC CAPITALS

| EGYPTIAN HIEROGLYPH | PHOENICIAN LETTER | GREEK LETTER | ROMAN LETTER | BASIC ITALIC | CURSIVE ITALIC CAPITAL |

A

5° slope

1st stroke: curve exit serif

3rd stroke: extended entrance of crossbar

OX

Algonquin·Anasazi·Apache·Arapaho

Names of Native American nations, tribes, and communities, past and present.

B

2nd stroke: curve entrance serif

HOUSE

Bannock·BellaCoola·Bilqula·Blackfeet

C

no change

CAMEL

Cayuga·Cherokee·Choctaw·Commanche

D

2nd stroke: curve entrance serif

DOOR

Dakota·Delaware·Duwamish

E

2nd stroke: curve entrance serif

BEHOLD

Eastern Shawnee·Erie·Eskimo

1 LOOK

2 PLAN

3 PRACTICE

CHECKLIST

____ letter shape
____ letter size
____ letter slope
____ letter spacing

Circle some of your best capitals.

	EGYPTIAN HIEROGLYPH	PHOENICIAN LETTER	GREEK LETTER	ROMAN LETTER	BASIC ITALIC	CURSIVE ITALIC CAPITAL

F

2nd stroke: curve entrance serif

Y (HOOK/NAIL) — F — F — F — F

Flathead · Fort Still Apache · Fox

G

changes to one-stroke: curve exit serif

(Added in the 3rd century BCE. The Romans added a bar to C to form G.)

G — G — G — or G

Gila · Goshute · Grosventres

H

1st stroke: sharp angle entrance serif, curve exit serif

2nd stroke: curve entrance serif begins slightly higher

3rd stroke: extended crossbar

H (FENCE) — H — H — H

Haida · Hopi · Hualapai · Huron

I

changes to one-stroke: horizontal entrance serif and exit serif

(HAND) — Z — S — I — I — I — or J

Illinois · Iowa · Iroquois · Isleta or Isleta

J

one stroke: horizontal entrance serif

(Added in the 16th century.)

J or J — J — J — or J

Jemez · Jicarilla or Jemez · Jicarilla

1 LOOK
2 PLAN
3 PRACTICE

CHECKLIST
____ letter shape
____ letter size
____ letter slope
____ letter spacing

✏ Circle some of your best capitals.

EGYPTIAN HIEROGLYPH	PHOENICIAN LETTER	GREEK LETTER	ROMAN LETTER	BASIC ITALIC	CURSIVE ITALIC CAPITAL

K

1st stroke: sharp angle entrance serif, curve exit serif

2nd stroke: curve exit serif

PALM

Kiowa · Klamath · Klickitat · Kwakiutl

L

one stroke: curve entrance serif, short exit serif

OX GOAD

Lakota or Lakota · Lillooet · Lumbee · Lummi

M

1st stroke: curve exit serif

WATER

Miami · Modoc · Mohawk · Munsee

N

1st stroke: curve exit serif

3rd stroke: soft curve entrance serif begins slightly higher

FISH

Navajo · Nez Perce · Nisqually · Nootka

O

no changes

EYE

Omaha · Oneida · Onondaga · Osage

1 LOOK
2 PLAN
3 PRACTICE
CHECKLIST
____ letter shape
____ letter size
____ letter slope
____ letter spacing

Circle some of your best capitals.

EGYPTIAN HIEROGLYPH	PHOENICIAN LETTER	GREEK LETTER	ROMAN LETTER	**BASIC ITALIC**	CURSIVE ITALIC CAPITAL

2nd stroke: curve entrance serif

MOUTH

Paiute · Pawnee · Potawatomi · Puyallup

2nd stroke: short exit serif

KNOT

Quapaw · Quechan · Quileute · Quinault

2nd stroke: curve entrance serif
3rd stroke: soft curve exit serif

HEAD

Rappahannock · Ree · Rosebud Sioux

no changes

TOOTH

Seneca · Shoshone · Sioux · Skokomish

2nd stroke: curve entrance serif

MARK/SIGN

Te-Moak · Tlingit · Tonkawa · Tuscarora

1 LOOK
2 PLAN
3 PRACTICE

CHECKLIST
____ letter shape
____ letter size
____ letter slope
____ letter spacing

Circle some of your best capitals.

	EGYPTIAN HIEROGLYPH	PHOENICIAN LETTER	GREEK LETTER	ROMAN LETTER	BASIC ITALIC	CURSIVE ITALIC CAPITAL

one-stroke: soft angle entrance serif

(Added in the 16th century.) U U U

Uinta · Umatilla · Umpqua · Ute

one-stroke: curve entrance serif

Y F V HOOK/NAIL V V V

one-stroke: curve entrance serif

W (Added in the 11th century.) W W W

Washoe · Wichita · Winnebago · Wyandotte

1st stroke: curve entrance serif and exit serif

╪ X X PROP X X X

Vilela · Viejas · Xip̃aya · Xixime
(Argentina)   (Brazil)   (Mexico)

changes to one-stroke: soft angle entrance serif, curve exit serif

Y Y Y HOOK/NAIL Y y Y

Yakima · Yaqui · Yomba · Yurok

one-stroke: short entrance serif and exit serif

Z Z Z Z SICKLE/WEAPON Z Z Z

Pueblo of Zia · Pueblo of Zuni

CHECKLIST
____ shape
____ size
____ slope
____ spacing

✎ Circle some of your best capitals.

Trace & copy.

1. First word in a sentence.

Always capitalize the first word in a
sentence. A

2. Names of people, places, and the pronoun I.

Ann · Brian · Copenhagen, Denmark · I
A

3. Names of peoples & languages.

African American · Asian · French
Hispanic/Latino · Native American
or Latina
A

Write names of other peoples.

4. Nouns and often adjectives referring to the Deity.

God · Jehovah · the Almighty
G

5. Names of sacred books.

Bible · Koran · Talmud · Vedas
B

6. Official titles— academic, business, government, nobility, & religious.

(used with name)
Mr. · Mrs. · Ms. · President.. Queen...
M

Write other titles.

7. Names of days of the week, months of the year, holidays, and holy days.

Monday · January · New Year's Day
Labor Day · Yom Kippur · Easter
M

Write other names.

8. Names of councils, expositions, and organizations.

Olympic Games · United Nations

9. Geographical terms that form part of a name.

Pacific Ocean · Main Street · Red Sea

10. Names of definite geographical divisions.

the Orient · Middle East · Northwest

11. Names of genera in botany and zoology— and all groups above genera.

Quercus *oak - Genus* · Rodentia *rat, squirrel - Order*

12. Names of planets, constellations, stars, and asteroids.

Sirius *star* · Taurus *constellation* · Uranus *planet* · Venus *planet* · Virgo *constellation*

13. Words in titles of books, poems, essays, or periodicals (except internal prepositions, conjunctions & articles).

The Wind in the Willows   *Underline titles of books or write book titles in all capitals.*

THE WIND IN THE WILLOWS   (SMALL CAPITALS)

14. First word of a salutation and complimentary close of a letter.

Dear Xina, · Sincerely, · Your Friend,

15. Words of a family relationship preceding name of a person.

Uncle Zeke · Grandma Yvonne

ABBREVIATIONS

LATIN   e.g. – for example (exempli gratia)

LATIN   etc. – and so forth (et cetera)

LATIN   i.e. – that is (id est)

LATIN   P.S. – to write after (postscriptus)

FRENCH   RSVP – please reply (respondez s'il vous plaît)

Answers to rebuses and riddle found on page 43.
REBUSES: all in one, you are too wise for me, square meal, he is underpaid. RIDDLE: Fannie Dooley likes words with double letters.

NUMERALS

The word NUMBER stands for an idea - how many objects in a certain group.
The word NUMERAL describes the symbol we use for the number idea.

Just as the first writing happened long after people began speaking, writing numerals to represent numbers came long after people began counting. The earliest numerals known were marks on stones and notches in sticks.

About 3,400 B.C. the Egyptians developed a written number system using hieroglyphics, as shown:

stroke ~ 1

arch ~ 10

coiled rope ~ 100

How would we write this? _____

One problem with the Egyptian system and those of the Greeks and the Romans is that none of them had a symbol to represent zero, "not any." In most early systems, people formed numerals by repeating a few basic symbols, then adding their values.

The numerals we use most likely came by way of Arabia from a starting point in India. The Hindus of India had a superior system—a base of ten and symbols for each number from one to nine. This was about 300 B.C. Probably about 900 years later they invented a symbol for zero. However, some sources give credit to Arabia for the zero. Later, these numerals arrived in Europe, first in Spain, and were developed into the system we use and that is used in most parts of the world today.

Beginning of our numerals

meaning no-thing

possibly from 7 stars in Big Dipper constellation

beginnings of 6, 8, & 9 unknown

HINDU-ARABIC NUMERALS
Use large numerals when writing with all large caps.

0 0 1 1 2 2 3 3 4 4 5 5 6 6 7 7 8 8 9 9

or 4

Use small numerals with lowercase and caps and for math.

0 1 2 3 4 5 6 7 8 9

ROMAN NUMERALS

Roman Numerals are written vertically with no slope.

I II III IV V VI VII VIII IX X XI XII

5-1=4   5   5+1=6   10-1=9   10   10+1=11

XX L C D M · MCMLXXXVIII

10+10=20   50   100   500   1,000   1000+(1000-100)+50+10+10+10+5+1+1+1=1988

Money amounts and metric system abbreviations

$15.27   98¢   6 cm   124 kg   539 km

centimeters   kilograms   kilometers

Time and temperature

8:30 a.m.   12:45 p.m.   74°F   30°C

ante meridian–before noon   post meridian–after noon   Fahrenheit   centigrade

Phone number, abbreviated date, height or length.

123 456-7890   3/20/94   5' 7"   8¾

area code   prefix   number   asterisk   fraction

Punctuation and other symbols

. , : ; ? ! " " — – ( ) ¢ $ ※ / & &

apostrophe   hyphen dash   parentheses   slant or slash   ampersands

POP-UP CARD

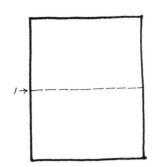  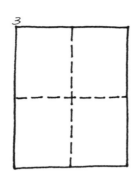 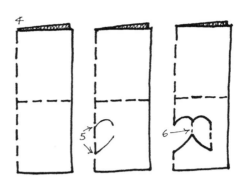

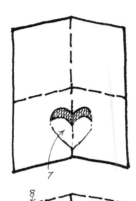

1. Fold 8 1/2" x 11" sheet of paper in half.
2. Fold paper in half again. Size is now 4 1/4" x 5 1/2".
3. Open paper to original size.
4. Fold in half lengthwise. Size is now 4 1/4" x 11".
5. Cut heart shape on fold of lower half (or tree, or geometric shape, etc.). Leave a part uncut to fold back.
6. Fold back heart.
7. Unfold to original position and open card. Bring fold forward by reversing fold to form heart inside card.
8. Fold top half down so it covers up hole (acts as a backing sheet). See position # 2.
9. Write on the pop-up shape, around the edge of the cut-out, on the front of the card—wherever you want!

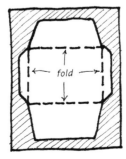

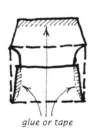

It is a joy to make your own cards with your own words and thoughts to send to your family and friends.

ENVELOPE

The 4 1/4" x 5 1/2" card fits perfectly in an A2 size envelope.

Make your own envelope. Open up an envelope. Spread it out and place it on a larger piece of paper. (Use strong paper such as shopping bags, magazine covers, gift wrap, construction paper, or butcher paper.) Trace around the edge. Cut out the new envelope. Fold like the original envelope. Glue or tape to hold together.

glue or tape

fold

See Envelope Pattern (A2 size), INSTRUCTION MANUAL, page 108.

Congratulations! You have complete this book! Turn to page viii and write you post-test using your best handwriting.

READING LOOPED CURSIVE
COMPARING GETTY-DUBAY CURSIVE ITALIC WITH LOOPED CURSIVE

NOTE: letter shape, letter slope, and size of capitals, ascenders, and descenders

CURSIVE ITALIC	LOOPED CURSIVE
5° slope	30° slope

Look at the examples of cursive italic and looped cursive. Compare the two styles of writing. Notice the differences in letter shape, letter slope, capital height, ascender height, and descender length.

There are many styles of writing you need to be able to read. Practice reading looped cursive. To help read the looped cursive letters, each name contains both a capital letter and its lowercase version.

SHAPE:
Look at the different shapes of the looped cursive lowercase letters b, f, r, s, and z and the capital letters F, G, I, J, Q, S, T, V, X, and Z.

SLOPE:
Look at the slope difference. Cursive Italic letter slope is 5° and looped cursive is 30° .

SIZE:
Look at the size difference. Cursive italic capitals, ascenders, and descenders are 1 1/2 body heights. Looped cursive capitals, ascenders and descenders are 2 body heights.

Compare the absence of loops in cursive italic with the many loops in looped cursive. Look at how the capitals, ascenders, and descenders become tangled in the looped cursive.
Loop-free italic is easier to read.

CURSIVE ITALIC	LOOPED CURSIVE
Angela	Angela
Barbara	Barbara
Cecilia	Cecilia
David	David
Eugene	Eugene
Fifi	Fifi
Gregory	Gregory
Hannah	Hannah
Irving	Irving
Jojo	Jojo
Kirk	Kirk
Lillian	Lillian
Malcolm	Malcolm
Nancy	Nancy
Otto	Otto
Philippa	Philippa
Quequeg	Quequeg
Richard	Richard
Susan	Susan
Trent	Trent
Ursula	Ursula
Vivian	Vivian
Woodrow	Woodrow
Xerxes	Xerxes
Yonny	Yonny
Zanzi	Zanzi

5mm lines

© 2012 Getty-Dubay
Getty-Dubay Italic Handwriting Series
available from Allport Editions: **www.allport.com/gdp**

© 2012 Getty-Dubay
Getty-Dubay Italic Handwriting Series
available from Allport Editions: **www.allport.com/gdp**